# Buying a new house

By Jenny Giles                    Photographs by Bill Thomas

## Monday

Mom said that Grandma was coming to stay with us. She will be staying with us for a long time.

I love my Grandma.

3

# Tuesday

Mom and Dad want to buy a bigger house for us.

Our house has two bedrooms. I sleep in this bedroom with my brother, Ben.

We are going to buy a new house with a bedroom for Grandma.

## Wednesday

Today we went for a ride
in the car.
We saw lots of houses.

I liked the white house best.

FOR SALE
PARKWOOD
REAL ESTATE

## Thursday

We went to see
the white house again.

We looked over the fence.
We saw a lot of grass
for Ben and me to play on.

We will go inside the house
in the morning.

## Friday

We went inside the house today.
It had a little bedroom upstairs
for me,
and a bigger one for Ben.

It had a good bedroom
for Grandma downstairs.

## Saturday

Grandma came to have a look
at the house today.
She liked it.

We all like this house.

## Sunday

Mom and Dad are going to buy the white house.
It will be our new home.

We are very happy.

I'm going to take my toy car to our new house.
Ben is going to take his bike.

We will have fun.